Guitar Initial

Pieces & Exercises

for Trinity College London examinations

2010-2015

Published by
Trinity College London

Registered Office:
4th floor, 89 Albert Embankment
London SE1 7TP UK

T +44 (0)20 7820 6100
F +44 (0)20 7820 6161
E music@trinitycollege.co.uk
www.trinitycollege.co.uk

Registered in the UK
Company no. 02683033
Charity no. 1014792

Copyright © 2009 Trinity College London
Fifth impression, February 2014

Printed in England by Halstan, Amersham, Bucks.

The Drunken Sailor

Traditional English

Frère Jacques

Traditional French

2

Minuet

from *The Anna Magdalena Notebook*

Johann Sebastian Bach
(1685-1750)

To a Wild Rose

Edward MacDowell
(1860-1908)

Cat Burglar

Gary Ryan
(born 1969)

To be played entirely with the right-hand thumb. All chords to be strummed lightly and quickly.
(*1*) Look over your shoulder.

Cactus Sunset

Phil Fentimen

Minor Mood

Roger Montgomery
(born 1947)

Get Up Get Down

Nicholas Powlesland

King of the Jungle

Lee Sollory
(born 1959)

Technical Suite (Exercises)

Candidates choosing Option ii) Technical Suite in the Technical Work section of the examination must prepare the following exercises.

1. Roller Coaster (scales)

To be prepared *apoyando* or *tirando* at candidate's choice.*

2. A Minor Moment (string crossing)

To be prepared *apoyando* or *tirando* at candidate's choice.

* *apoyando* = rest stroke; *tirando* = free stroke.

3. Deep End of the Pool (thumb articulation)

To be prepared *apoyando* or *tirando* at candidate's choice. Played with RH thumb.

4. Right Hand Exercises

a)

To be prepared *tirando*.

b)

To be prepared *tirando*.